STAR WARS®
INVASION

THE NEW JEDI ORDER
(25–40 years after the Battle of Yavin)

As this era began, Luke Skywalker had unified the Jedi Order into a cohesive group of powerful Jedi Knights. It was a time of relative peace, yet darkness approached on the horizon. Now, Skywalker's descendants face new and resurgent threats to the galaxy, and to the balance of the Force.

The events in this story take place approximately twenty-five years after the Battle of Yavin.

STAR WARS® INVASION

1 REFUGEES

Script
TOM TAYLOR

Art
COLIN WILSON

Colors
WES DZIOBA

Letters
MICHAEL HEISLER

Cover Art
JO CHEN

DARK HORSE BOOKS®

president and publisher
MIKE RICHARDSON

collection designer
SCOTT COOK

editor
RANDY STRADLEY

assistant editor
FREDDYE LINS

NEIL HANKERSON executive vice president TOM WEDDLE chief financial officer RANDY STRADLEY vice president of publishing MICHAEL MARTENS vice president of business development ANITA NELSON vice president of marketing, sales, and licensing DAVID SCROGGY vice president of product development DALE LAFOUNTAIN vice president of information technology DARLENE VOGEL director of purchasing KEN LIZZI general counsel DAVEY ESTRADA editorial director SCOTT ALLIE senior managing editor CHRIS WARNER senior books editor DIANA SCHUTZ executive editor CARY GRAZZINI director of design and production LIA RIBACCHI art director CARA NIECE director of scheduling

special thanks to Jann Moorhead, David Anderman, Troy Alders, Leland Chee, Sue Rostoni, and Carol Roeder at Lucas Licensing

STAR WARS: INVASION—REFUGEES volume 1

This volume collects issues #0–#5 of the Dark Horse comic-book series *Star Wars: Invasion*.

Published by
Dark Horse Books
A division of Dark Horse Comics, Inc.
10956 SE Main Street
Milwaukie, OR 97222

darkhorse.com
starwars.com

To find a comics shop in your area, call the Comic Shop Locator Service toll-free at 1-888-266-4226

Library of Congress Cataloging-in-Publication Data

Refugees / script Tom Taylor ; art Colin Wilson ; colors Wes Dzioba ; letters Michael Heisler ; cover art Jo Chen.
-- 1st ed.
p. cm. -- (Star Wars--Invasion ; v. 1)
Summary: "Approximately twenty-five years after the Battle of Yavin, the galaxy has been rid of the evil Empire, and a New Republic has been formed. Jedi Master Luke Skywalker is rebuilding the Jedi Order, and has formed a Jedi Academy to train new students as Jedi Knights, protectors of the weak and upholders of peace. Still, not all is right in the galaxy. While the Sith are no longer a threat, there are other things to fear."
ISBN 978-1-59582-479-0
1. Star Wars fiction--Comic books, strips, etc. 2. Graphic novels. I. Wilson, Colin, 1949 Oct. 31- II. Heisler, Michael. III. Dark Horse Comics.
PN6728.S73R44 2010
741.5'973--dc22
                2009051284

First edition: May 2010
ISBN: 978-1-59582-479-0

1 3 5 7 9 10 8 6 4 2
Printed at Midas Printing International, Ltd., Huizhou, China

Approximately twenty-five years after the Battle of Yavin, the galaxy has been rid of the evil Empire, and a New Republic has been formed.

Jedi Master Luke Skywalker is rebuilding the Jedi Order, and has formed a Jedi Academy to train new students as Jedi Knights, protectors of the weak and upholders of peace.

Still, not all is right in the galaxy. While the Sith are no longer a threat, there are other things to fear . . .

REFUGEES

ILLUSTRATION BY DAVE DORMAN

APPROXIMATELY TWENTY-FIVE YEARS AFTER THE BATTLE OF YAVIN.

SOMEWHERE AT THE EDGE OF A GALAXY FAR, FAR AWAY...

SARKKIN, WHERE ARE YOU?

...TWO EXPLORERS SEARCH THE UNKNOWN.

SARKKIN, ARE YOU ALL RIGHT?

‹FOR WHATEVER REASON, THEY WANTED TO TAKE US ALIVE. I DON'T THINK WE SHOULD LET THEM TRY AGAIN.›

NO.

‹I DON'T THINK SO. NO.›

THEY WERE EXPLORERS. THEY DISCOVERED SOMETHING BEFORE ANYONE ELSE. THEY SACRIFICED EVERYTHING TO SHARE THAT DISCOVERY WITH THE PEOPLE WHO NEEDED IT MOST.

COMMANDER AZCA, THE SHIP IS COMING THIS WAY. THE BOARDING PARTY MUST HAVE SEIZED CONTROL ALREADY.

GOOD.

WHA--? THEY'RE PICKING UP SPEED!

WHY DID THEY BOARD US? THEY COULD HAVE JUST BLASTED US OUT OF SPACE.

AND, THOUGH NO ONE WOULD EVER HEAR OF IT --

-- THEIR LAST DESPERATE ACT OF DEFIANCE WAS ONE OF THE FIRST STRIKES AGAINST THE YUUZHAN VONG.

A RUINED YORIC-VEC DRIFTS AWAY FROM THE BLAST. THE ONCE-LIVING SHIP, NOW DEAD.

ON BOARD, THE FEROCIOUS **TSALOK** STANDS AMIDST HIS BROKEN CREW. HIS BODY IS RACKED WITH PAIN AS HE TASTES THE FRESH BLOOD THAT TRICKLES DOWN HIS FACE.

THIS NEW GALAXY HAS WELCOMED TSALOK WITH *VIOLENCE* AND *DEATH.*

HE LIKES IT ALREADY.

ON NAR SHADDAA, THE SMUGGLERS' MOON, AN IMPORTANT TRANSACTION TAKES PLACE.

AMIDST THE INVASION FLEET, A VONG SLAVE-SHIP COMMANDER MERCILESSLY BEATS THE LAST SURVIVOR OF A WARRIOR RACE.

WHILE ON YAVIN 4, LUKE SKYWALKER FEELS A GREAT DARKNESS APPROACHING. A DARKNESS ALREADY RESPONSIBLE FOR HIS WIFE'S ILLNESS.

BELOW HIM, HAN AND LEIA'S CHILDREN TRAIN IN THE WAYS OF THE JEDI.

DESPITE ALL OF HIS POWER, LUKE ISN'T SURE HE CAN PROTECT HIS SISTER'S CHILDREN. A NEW TYPE OF EVIL IS ENTERING THE GALAXY.

THEIR CHILDHOOD IS AT AN END.

YUUZHAN VONG.

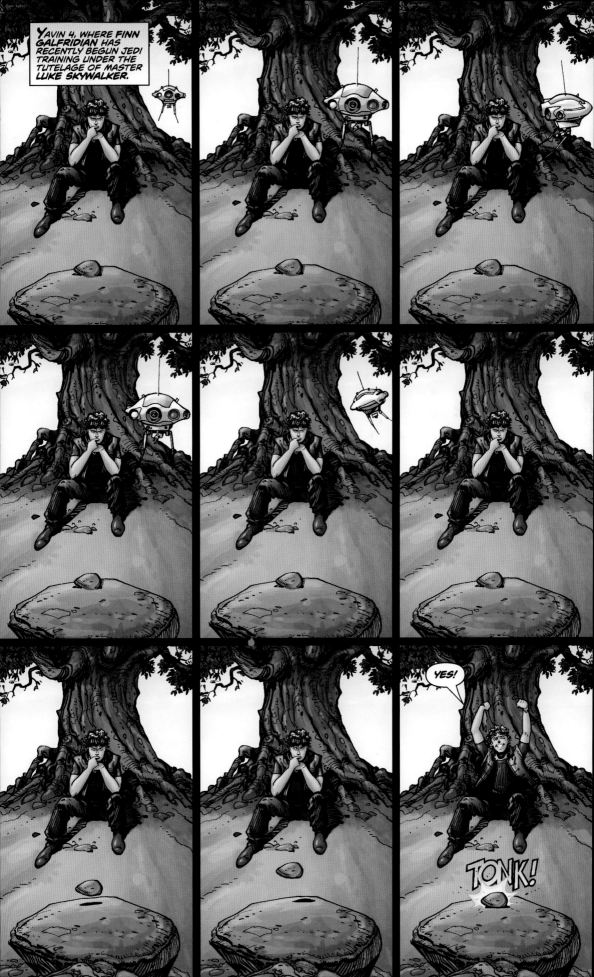

THE YUUZHAN VONG SLAVE SHIP TSAM P'AH. CURRENTLY IN ORBIT AROUND ARTORIAS --

-- WHERE FINN'S MOTHER NINA AND SISTER KAYE ARE BEING HELD IN APPALLING CONDITIONS.

YOU ARE QUEEN?

THIS WOMAN NEEDS MEDICAL ATTENTION.

NO. SHE WILL DIE. YOU WILL COME.

NO. I WON'T.

ALLOW HIM TO CONFRONT HIS ENEMY FACE-TO-FACE. WE'LL SEE FOR OURSELVES WHETHER HE GIVES IN TO HATE.

WE MUST TRUST IN THE FORCE. WE WILL KNOW WHEN HE IS READY.

IF HE'S NOT READY... IF SOMETHING HAPPENED, IT WOULD BE A WASTE.

TONK TONK TONK

WHAT'S THIS?

IT'S MY ROCK.

LUKE SKYWALKER.

A SIMPLE FARM BOY --

-- BECAME POWERFUL.

NOW, BEYOND POWERFUL.

"MASTER LE'UNG, THIS IS AIR SUPPORT. WE HAVE ONE OF THE CREATURES IN OUR SIGHTS."

HHSSSSSSSS

"PILOT, BE CAREFUL. THIS CREATURE IS MORE THAN IT SEEMS."

--YUUZHAN VONG ARE INVISIBLE TO THE FORCE.

ARTORIAS. FINN'S FORMER HOME IS BARELY RECOGNIZABLE. THE FORESTS ARE GONE, THE PLANET STILL SMOLDERS FROM THE FIREBREATHERS AND THE VONGFORMING HAS BEGUN.

AN EXPLOSION ROCKS THE HEART OF THE YUUZHAN VONG BIOTECH, DISRUPTING THE TERRAFORMING OF THE PLANET.

KOOOMM

IT IS NOT THE FIRST ATTACK, BUT THE YUUZHAN VONG ARE STILL CLUELESS AS TO THE PERPETRATORS.

THE SOUND OF THE IMMENSE BLAST IS EVEN LOUD ENOUGH TO REACH *DULAC*, A FRIEND AND ADVISOR TO FINN'S FATHER--

BUT THIS IS NOT TO BE THE END OF DULAC'S SUFFERING.

THERE IS FAR MORE TO COME.

-- EVEN THROUGH THE INCREDIBLE, INDESCRIBABLE PAIN.

ARGGHHI

TRUE NATURES ARE REVEALED AT TIMES LIKE THIS.

YOU TOOK MY *FAMILY,* MY *FRIENDS,* AND MY *HOME!*

NOT JUST RESTRAINT OR IMPULSIVENESS... BUT LIGHT OR DARK.

GOOD OR EVIL.

TO TAKE THE LIFE OF A SWORN ENEMY IN THIS SITUATION MIGHT NOT BE PERCEIVED AS EVIL.

NNNAAAGHHHHH!

LUKE SKYWALKER UNDERSTANDS. HE WILL NOT JUDGE FINN GALFRIDIAN BY THIS ONE ACT.

NO MERCY COULD BE EXPECTED --

-- BUT SOME INDIVIDUALS EXCEED EXPECTATIONS.

<I DON'T...?>

AND SOME SMALL ACTIONS HAVE LARGE, UNFORESEEN REPERCUSSIONS.

LEARN.

WELL DONE.

LET'S JUST GET OUT OF HERE.

TSALOK CAN'T COMPREHEND WHAT HAS JUST HAPPENED. HE WAS SUPPOSED TO DIE.

‹COMMANDER TSALOK, THESE MEN ARE TOO OLD OR WEAK TO SERVE THE YUUZHAN VONG.›

TSALOK HAS NEVER HEARD OF MERCY, LET ALONE EMPLOYED IT --

WAIT!

-- HE IS NOT ABOUT TO START NOW.

TSALOK SHOULD BE DEAD.

HE NOW COMMANDS A **WORLD,** BUT IT FEELS...HOLLOW.

HE OWES HIS LIFE TO ANOTHER. TO A SWORN ENEMY.

HE MUST KNOW WHY. HE MUST SEEK OUT THIS JEEDAI --

-- HE MUST HURT HIM UNTIL HE GIVES HIM THE ANSWERS HE SEEKS.

YOU *COULD* HELP US, YOU KNOW?

SHOW-OFF.

YOU'RE CALLING *ME* A SHOW-OFF? HAVE YOU FORGOTTEN WHO YOU'RE *MARRIED* TO?

I DON'T SUPPOSE HAN...?

NO. HE'S LENT US THE *FALCON*, BUT HE WON'T BE JOINING US.

*"LEIA, CHEWBACCA *DIED* AT THE HANDS OF THE YUUZHAN VONG. AN *ENTIRE PLANET* DIED THAT DAY. THERE'S A HIGH PROBABILITY THAT, *HAD* ANAKIN ATTEMPTED A RESCUE, *HE* WOULD HAVE DIED, TOO."

*"HAN ISN'T DOING WELL --"

*"I KNOW, BUT HE *CAN'T* BLAME HIS SON...NOT FOREVER."

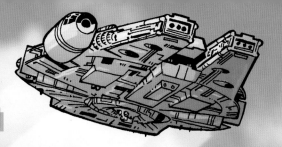

"--PUNCH IT!"

WHAT ARE YOU THINKING ABOUT, FARM BOY?

YOU SHOULD BE RESTING. THE DISEASE...

YOU SHOULD BE RESTING. I DOUBT YOU REMEMBER THE LAST TIME YOU STOPPED.

COME, *HUSBAND*. HOPEFULLY, ONE DAY, YOU'LL HAVE THE OPPORTUNITY TO BE A DISAPPOINTMENT TO YOUR *OWN* SON.

I'M THINKING ABOUT FATHERS AND SONS, MARA. FATHERS AND SONS...AND DISAPPOINTMENT.

THE YUUZHAN VONG HAVE CONQUERED THIS PLANET LIKE SO MANY MORE. QUICKLY. EASILY. BUT ON ARTORIAS TONIGHT, ONCE AGAIN, DARK THINGS RISE FROM THE GREAT SEA.

THE YUUZHAN VONG ARE WARRIORS AT HEART. THEY ARE **BUILT** FOR BATTLE.

THEY **GRAFT** BIOTECH TO THEIR OWN BODIES TO MAKE THEMSELVES MORE FORMIDABLE -- MORE INTIMIDATING.

ALL OF THEIR TECHNOLOGY IS ALIVE --

-- YET, ALL OF THIS LIVING TECHNOLOGY HAS BEEN SHAPED FOR ONE THING...DEATH.

IN TRUTH, THE YUUZHAN VONG WOULD PREFER GREATER RESISTANCE FROM THEIR CONQUERED FOES.

ON ARTORIAS, THEY HAVE FOUND THAT RESISTANCE. THERE IS SOMETHING HERE THAT IS OUT OF THEIR CONTROL. THERE IS SOMETHING HERE THAT CANNOT BE EASILY DEFEATED. AFTER ALL, HOW DO YOU DEFEAT SOMETHING WHEN YOU DON'T KNOW WHAT IT IS?

HOW DO YOU FIGHT SOMETHING THAT DOESN'T SEEM TO EXIST?

BUT THE DESTRUCTION AND CHAOS ARE REAL ENOUGH.

WELCOME TO *NAR SHADDAA*. NICE PLACE -- IF YOU DON'T MIND WAKING UP MISSING SOME ORGANS.

I NEED TO MEET WITH SOMEONE WE HAVE IN THE CITY. THEY'RE SUPPOSED TO SUPPLY US WITH SOME INFORMATION ON OUR SMUGGLER.

WHO DO WE HAVE *HERE*?

IT'S NOT IMPORTANT. FEEL FREE TO WANDER AROUND THE MAIN PART OF THE CITY. DON'T INSULT ANYBODY AND, WHATEVER YOU DO, *DON'T EAT ANYTHING.*

AND IF ANYONE OFFERS TO SELL YOU A *DEEB*, ANAKIN, YOU'RE TOO YOUNG. LOWBACCA, IT WOULDN'T AFFECT YOU. JAINA, YOU WOULDN'T LIKE IT, AND JACEN...*YOU'RE NOT ALLOWED.*

WHAT ABOUT ME?

I'M NOT IN CHARGE OF YOU, FINN. BUT IF YOU GET A BAD ONE, I'M NOT COLLECTING THE *PIECES* OF YOU THAT *FALL OFF.*

THEY SAY ONCE YOU'VE BEEN TO NAR SHADDAA, YOU'LL WANT TO STAY FOREVER. THAT'S NOT ENTIRELY TRUE...THAT'S JUST WHAT THEY TELL THE FAMILIES OF ALL OF THE PEOPLE WHO GO MISSING HERE.

HELLO. I AM DAHAL. YOU LOOK INNOCENT. LET ME BE YOUR GUIDE.

WE'RE NOT AS INNOCENT AS WE MAY LOOK.

NO ONE IS.

HANG ON. BLAST! PROWL IS BACK IN THE HANGAR. YOU GO AHEAD. I'LL CATCH UP.

ARE YOU SURE?

HE'S SURE! FOLLOW DAHAL. WE WILL BUY SOMETHING ...OR SOMEONE. THE VERTICAL CITY WILL BE OURS.

...MACHINE...

THERE HAS BEEN SO MUCH UNCERTAINTY IN FINN'S LIFE. HE HAS HAD TOO MUCH TIME TO THINK, TO PONDER ON THE FATES OF FAMILY AND FRIENDS.

IT'S A STRANGE REVELATION, AS HE MOVES SILENTLY THROUGH THIS CITY THAT WOULD KILL HIM FOR HIS SHOES, BUT HAVING ONE CLEAR OBJECTIVE, ONE CLEAR FOCUS, IS LIBERATING.

...MISSION.

JUST MAN...

ON THE SLAVE SHIP TSAM P'AH, THERE HAVE BEEN MANY CASUALTIES.

ARBELOA HAS FOUGHT LIKE A DEMON AGAINST THESE MONSTERS. YET EVEN HE IS BEGINNING TO TIRE.

BUT WITH EACH CELL OPENED --

-- MORE ALLIES ARE GAINED.

THE YUUZHAN VONG ARE FIERCE, BUT THEY ARE FEW.

THE TABLES ARE TURNING.

FAR FROM THE FIGHTING, A QUEEN SURVEYS HER FORMER REALM. THE PAIN OF LOSS THAT HAS PARALYZED HER FOR SO LONG IS FORGOTTEN AS SHE SEES THE DAMAGED VONG BUILDINGS.

IN THAT MOMENT SHE KNOWS...

ARTORIAS DOES NOT BELONG TO THE YUUZHAN VONG.

THE FIGHT IS ALMOST OVER. THE PRISONERS HAVE REACHED THE COMMAND CENTER AND THE MAN WHO IMPRISONED THEM ALL...

COMMANDER SHA'KEL.

PRINCESS.

I PROMISED THIS MAN YOUR HEAD.

IT'S LUCKY YOU LIKE PAIN.

BECAUSE THIS IS GOING TO *HURT*.

"IT'S ALL RIGHT, KAYE..."

"IT'S DONE."

the end of INVASION: REFUGEES

STAR WARS®

ILLUSTRATION BY JO CHEN

STAR WARS® VECTOR

An event with repercussions for every era and every hero in the *Star Wars* galaxy begins here! For anyone who never knew where to start with *Star Wars* comics, *Vector* is the perfect introduction to the entire *Star Wars* line! For any serious *Star Wars* fan, *Vector* is a must-see event with major happenings throughout the most important moments of the galaxy's history!

VOLUME ONE
(*Knights of the Old Republic* Vol. 5; *Dark Times* Vol. 3)
ISBN 978-1-59582-226-0 | $17.99

VOLUME TWO
(*Rebellion* Vol. 4; *Legacy* Vol. 6)
ISBN 978-1-59582-227-7 | $17.99

KNIGHTS OF THE OLD REPUBLIC
Volume One: Commencement
ISBN 978-1-59307-640-5 | $18.99

Volume Two: Flashpoint
ISBN 978-1-59307-761-7 | $18.99

Volume Three: Days of Fear, Nights of Anger
ISBN 978-1-59307-867-6 | $18.99

Volume Four: Daze of Hate, Knights of Suffering
ISBN 978-1-59582-208-6 | $18.99

Volume Six: Vindication
ISBN 978-1-59582-274-1 | $19.99

Volume Seven: Dueling Ambitions
ISBN 978-1-59582-348-9 | $18.99

Volume Eight: Destroyer
ISBN 978-1-59582-419-6 | $17.99

REBELLION
Volume One: My Brother, My Enemy
ISBN 978-1-59307-711-2 | $14.99

Volume Two: The Ahakista Gambit
ISBN 978-1-59307-890-4 | $17.99

Volume Three: Small Victories
ISBN 978-1-59582-166-9 | $12.99

LEGACY
Volume One: Broken
ISBN 978-1-59307-716-7 | $17.99

Volume Two: Shards
ISBN 978-1-59307-879-9 | $19.99

Volume Three: Claws of the Dragon
ISBN 978-1-59307-946-8 | $17.99

Volume Four: Alliance
ISBN 978-1-59582-223-9 | $15.99

Volume Five: The Hidden Temple
ISBN 978-1-59582-224-6 | $15.99

Volume Seven: Storms
ISBN 978-1-59582-350-2 | $17.99

Volume Eight: Tatooine
ISBN 978-1-59582-414-1 | $17.99

DARK TIMES
Volume One: The Path to Nowhere
ISBN 978-1-59307-792-1 | $17.99

Volume Two: Parallels
ISBN 978-1-59307-945-1 | $17.99

Volume Four: Blue Harvest
ISBN 978-1-59582-264-2 | $17.99

darkhorse.com

DARK HORSE BOOKS

AVAILABLE AT YOUR LOCAL COMICS SHOP OR BOOKSTORE.
TO FIND A COMICS SHOP IN YOUR AREA, CALL 1-888-266-4226
For more information or to order direct: On the web: darkhorse.com
E-mail: mailorder@darkhorse.com • Phone: 1-800-862-0052 Mon.–Fri.
9 AM to 5 PM Pacific Time. STAR WARS © 2004–2010 Lucasfilm Ltd. & ™ (BL8005)

STAR WARS EMPIRE

DARK HORSE COMICS

TO FIND A COMICS SHOP IN YOUR AREA, CALL 1-888-266-4226.
For more information or to order direct:
*On the web: darkhorse.com
*E-mail: mailorder@darkhorse.com
*Phone: 1-800-862-0052 Mon.-Fri. 9 A.M. to 5 P.M. Pacific Time.